Puppy and the Sausage

Puppy and the Sausage

Gabriel Fitzmaurice

Illustrations by
Stewart Curry

FOR CHILDREN

Published 1998 by
Poolbeg Press Ltd
123 Baldoyle Industrial Estate
Dublin 13, Ireland

Reprinted March 1999
Reprinted June 2000

Text © Gabriel Fitzmaurice 1998
Illustrations © Stewart Curry 1998

The moral right of the author has been asserted.

The Arts Council
An Chomhairle Ealaíon

A catalogue record for this book is available from the British Library.

ISBN 1 85371 858 0

Illustrations by Stewart Curry
Cover design by Poolbeg Group Services Ltd
Set by Poolbeg Group Services Ltd in AGaramond 12/14
Printed by The Guernsey Press Ltd,
Vale, Guernsey, Channel Islands.

For Nessa and John for being my muses
and George who ate the sausage
and Fluffy who drank the suds
and Sandy who jumped the wire
and Dandelion
and for Percy and Goldie who died

Contents

What's in a Name?

I'm Gabriel Fitzmaurice –
God, how I hate that name!
Fitzmaurice is not too bad,
But Gabriel's a pain.

When my parents named me,
They didn't ask my views –
If they asked me now I'd tell them
I should have been *Ted Hughes*,

Two syllables, two strong vowels:
The tongue-twister they gave me
Is polite and sissy-ish
And not at all like me.

I'm Gabriel Fitzmaurice –
When I had a son,
Did I call him *Gabriel*?
No way! I called him *John* –

We chose his name – a single sound
As strong as vowels can be,
He'll never have to fight his way
Through a flowery name like me.

I'm Gabriel Fitzmaurice –
A name I've made my own;
A name that I can live with,
A name through which I've grown.

I'm Gabriel Fitzmaurice,
I no longer hate my name –
Fitzmaurice is my history
(But Gabriel's still a pain!).

Saturday Morning

Mammy in Dublin
And John not at home –
Just Nessa and Daddy
All on our own.

Nessa gets cornflakes,
Dad makes the tea,
We sit down to breakfast
Quiet as can be.

Not like some mornings
All bustle and fuss –
It's Saturday morning,
Today it's just us.

Crack! go the cornflakes,
Plop! goes the tea –
Saturday morning,
Just Daddy and me.

A Song for Myself

There was no one at home I could play with
So I washed and I dried up the delph;
There was nothing else there to amuse me
So I sang a song for myself.

And when I told Mammy and Daddy
I was singing a song and just why,
They smiled and they asked me to sing it
But I couldn't 'cos I was too shy.

I Wish I Was a Kettle

I wish I was a kettle
'Cos kettles feel no pain;
They never sick, they never cry,
They never feel the strain

Of being five and frightened,
They just sit on the hob
Until they put to boiling
Then get on with the job.

I wish I was a kettle
(I can't stop crying, Dad –
I've a bad pain in my tummy
And I very feeling mad).

Brushing Her Hair

When Mammy gets the brush
She's in an awful rush
She pulls it through the tangles in my hair
And there is no escape
Although you stamp and scrape.
When it's brushed I mess it up. So there!

Daddy's Belly

Daddy got a belly,
It's very stickin'-out,
An' Mammy says he got it
From drinkin' too much stout.

Daddy's very cuddly –
He's like a teddy bear,
Safe an' soft an' spongy,
Curly kind of hair.

Daddy got a belly,
He's goin' on a diet –
Mammy said he better
An' Daddy said he try it.

Daddy got a belly
But soon he will be thinner
Drinkin' no more porter
An' eatin' lot less dinner.

Daddy's Doggy

Daddy pats me like a dog
When I'm being good –
Like when I clean the budgies' cage
Or give the hamster food.

Daddy pats me like a dog
But it drives me **mad** –
Some day I'll just burst out and say:
"I'm not your doggy, Dad!"

A Goodnight Kiss

I pulled my sister's hair,
I hit her with my shoe;
Daddy's very mad at me –
I know what he'll do:

No story when it's bedtime,
A kiss will have to do
For, though he's very mad at me,
Dad loves bold boys too.

I Like the Day, I Fear the Night

I like the day,
I fear the night
But ghosts and goblins
Don't frighten me,
Nor scary programmes on TV.
What scares me most
Is me.

When I'm settled in my bed,
These scary things
Start in my head;
And though I know
That they're not there,
They scare me.

And Mam and Daddy
Stay beside me
Till all is safe
Again inside me.

Waddi

When you get in Daddy's bed
And he hugs you, rubs your head
That's *Waddi*

When you're snugly cuddly cosy
And your mind is swimming dozy
That's *Waddi*

When you're tucked in safe and warm
Know the night will bring no harm
That's *Waddi*
        Waddi
            Waddi

Her First Flight

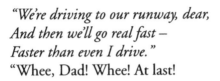

"I love you, Dad! I love you!
I love this massive plane –
It looks like a big fat pencil-case
(Aer Spain – is it, Dad? Aer Spain?).

This aeroplane's exciting,
It's noise-ing up to go –
Will it drive as fast as you, Dad?
But Dad – we're going slow."

"We're driving to our runway, dear,
And then we'll go real fast –
Faster than even I drive."
"Whee, Dad! Whee! At last!

We're going really speedy,
When are we going to fly?
Wow! Up, up, up we go, Dad!
'Way up in the sky.

What's happening to my ears, Dad?
They're funny – I can't hear
(Well, kind of); what you say, Dad?
There's something in my ears."

"Suck a sweet, 'twill help you –
It's a good idea."
"Who's Eddie, Daddy? Eddie?"
"I said it's a good idea.

Look at the clouds now, Nessa:
We're coming to them – just;
In a minute we'll be through them."
"Dad! It's like they're made of dust–

The clouds are awful dusty,
I can't see a thing –
Just dark outside my window.
Now what's happening?

We're above the clouds! The sunshine!"
"Sit back now and relax.
It's three hours to Tenerife –
Let's have a little nap."

"Daddy, we're not moving –
Look down at the sea:
It's not moving, we're not moving;
This is boring – I have my wee!

Daddy, where's the toilet?
I'm bored with this oul' plane."
"Look out the window, Nessa –
Look down and you'll see Spain."

"Daddy, where's the toilet?
Is there any on this plane?"
"OK, OK, I'll take you;"
"Daddy, we're over Spain . . .

When I was at the toilet,
I made poops as well as wee –
Where did the poops go, Daddy?
The poops I made, the wee?

Did they fall down on some Spanish man
'Way 'way down below?
Where did my poops go, Daddy?
Where did my wee-wee go?

What's next after Spain, Dad?
Will we get our dinner soon?
This aeroplane's exciting.
How far up is the moon?

Dad, my ears are popping –
Is everything all right?
Daddy, oops! I chewed my sweet
I got such an awful fright.

But it's OK now, Daddy –
It's just the plane going down.
Daddy, Daddy! Tenner Reef!
Dad, is this our town?"

Thank God for McDonald's

Dad wasn't into McDonald's –
When he said it, his lip kinda curled:
"They taste all the same
At home and in Spain –
That crowd'll take over the world."

Dad wasn't into McDonald's –
When he went to a place, he would eat
Local food: "Local food!
Ah! It's part of the mood –
I consider such cooking a treat."

Dad wasn't into McDonald's
Till he took us out foreign one year:
He thought us quite rude
To refuse local food
(In a wine place *he* wouldn't drink beer!).

Oh! Dad wasn't into McDonald's
Till we couldn't even eat local bread;
He sighed "Well, OK –
Let's do it your way."
("Thank God for McDonald's," he said!)

Onions

Onions!
Oh, I love onions!
I could talk all day about onions:

I could tell you the story of the onion
Who flew up to the top of a mosque
And stayed there like a prayer
Till the builders set it there
Forever;

Or I could tell you the story of the onion
Who thought he was a turnip
But wasn't –
He jumped into bed with the turnips
But the turnips killed him.
(There was a big *turn-up* at the funeral.)

I love onions –

I love their crackle and their sting
When you peel them ring by ring
And tears fill up your eyes

(I eat them raw)

And they burn in your nose
And they tingle to your toes.
I love onions.

I love onions for a treat,

I love onions with my meat,
I love onions boiled or fried
But I don't like (though I've tried)
Onions grilled – they're far too dry
(I like 'em juicy); but, oh boy!
The way I like 'em best of all
Is to take one, big or small,
And munch it raw with a little drink
Then get in close and breathe the stink
In my daddy's eyes and nose
And then chuckle "Smell the rose!"
Daddy starts up and he goes
"Go away! Just go away!
Ugh! The children of today . . . "

Cuts

"Dad, d'you want to see my cuts?"
"I'm looking – show me, dear."
"Daddy – look! I got two cuts
Here and here and here."

"How many cuts is that, my love?"
"Daddy – one, two, three."
"But first you told me you had two."
"Oh, Daddy, silly me!"

Pins and Needles

My leg is kinda fizzy
It's tingling toe by toe
My ankle's feeling dizzy
Will the prickles ever go?
My toes are in a tizzy
Ooooooh!

Confessions of a Thumb Sucker

Everyone tries to stop me –
They say that it looks dumb,
But always when I'm idle
I suck my thumb.

And when everything about me
Is grumpy, gammy, glum,
When adults take out the tablets:
I suck my thumb.

My thumb is kinda dreamy,
When **BIGHUGE** problems come
My eyes turn in and look within
As I suck my thumb.

Luddle-Uddle-Uddle

My baby brother has no teeth
He can only nibble
I can't make out a thing he says
Because he's talking scribble

S397955

Nora

Nora sits in the Old Folks' Home,
She's very old and all alone;
She doesn't even know her friends,
This is how the twilight ends.

Her mouth's a hole where once it smiled
On me and every little child,
Her eyes are open wide and stare –
She doesn't even know who's there.

But Granda sits and holds her hands.
He says that Nora understands,
He sits like that an hour or more;
Sometimes her breath is like a snore,
She wears a thing to keep her head
From falling down before she's dead.
He sits beside her in a chair
He doesn't talk, he just sits there –
Granda sits and holds her hands,
Sometimes she looks and understands.

The Old Tree

The old tree's still standing down Barney's *boreen*.
It's taller than houses and always is green,
No one comes near it, but the kids in his day
Would meet there at evening, swap stories and play;
And sometimes they'd climb it 'way up to the top
Where the branches would bend but never would snap,
And you'd see the whole parish for miles and for miles –
Granda remembers; he tells me and smiles.
When he was a child it reached to the sky
Now nobody climbs it, and he wonders why.

boreen: a narrow side road, a country lane

Will Granda Die?

"Will Granda die? He's getting old."
(I hug my little son)
"Oh, please don't say that he will die –
Don't children keep you young?"

Peggy's Leg

Peggy's leg – you ate it!
It was a kind of rock
Wrapped in "plastic paper",
Tuppence in the shop.

Conversation lozenges
With words that you could read,
Black Jack, bull's-eyes – yummy!
What more could you need?

Where are they now? – they've vanished;
Now what do you buy?
Monster Munchies, Banshee Bones
And sweets that shout with dye.

Peggy's leg has vanished;
So, too, the grocer's shop
That sold it to us children.
The world cannot stop.

The grocer's out on pension,
His shop is now a room
Where he watches television
In the evening gloom;

The grocer's out on pension,
Peggy's leg's no more . . .
How I miss the grocer
In his little store.

In Memoriam Danny Cunningham 1912–1995

I take her to the Funeral Home –
She wants to see him dead;
She's not afraid – she rubs his hands
And then explores his head.

"He not wake up I rub him.
Look, Daddy! He not move.
Where Danny, Dad?" she asks me.
"Danny's dead, my love."

"Where Danny, Dad?" she asks again;
Then suddenly it's clear –
"The old Danny in the box," she says;
"The new one – he not here."

Children's TV

I'm tired of robots on TV
And aliens who're not like me
Who don't feel happy, don't feel sad,
Who're just there to act up bad;

I wonder why TV cannot
Put more humans in the plot,
Humans who can think and feel,
Humans who are simply *real* –
Not some super kind of guy
Who, it seems, can never die.

I'm tired of programmes that excite,
And nothing more, by day, by night;
I want TV to make me sad,
Sympathise, to make me glad,
To make me love, to make me fear,
To make me think, to make me cheer –
To be a channel for all of me.
I'm tired of robots on TV.

Goalie

I'd like to be a goalie
(I let in all the goals
And everybody says to me
My hands are made of holes).

I'd like to be a goalie –
I'd be everybody's friend
'Cos I'd be on the football team.
Instead I just pretend.

Autograph

Big Liam Flaherty of Kerry,
The best centre-back in the game,
Played in our village last Sunday;
I asked him if he'd sign his name.

He told me that he'd be delighted,
But I had no paper or book
So I rolled up my sleeve and said "Liam,
You can write on my arm here, look!"

He signed his name in blue Biro.
My classmates all ask for a peek
And I roll up my sleeve and I show them –
Now I won't wash for a week!

The Lost Carrot

"I'm lost," said the carrot,
"I'm lost," said the parrot,
"I'm lost," said the carrot again;
"I'm lost," said the parrot,
"You're not," said the carrot,
"You're not," said the parrot,
"*I'm* lost," said the carrot
And it started all over again . . .

Smelly Socks and Hairy Legs

Smelly Socks and Hairy Legs
Met one day in a shoe;
They both smiled at each other,
Said Smelly: "How d'you do?"

"Do what? Do what?" said Hairy Legs,
"Do nothing!" Smelly smiled,
"I only meant 'How are you?'
There's no need to get riled."

"I see! I see!" said Hairy Legs,
"You're smelly – well, a little;"
"I'm sorry, friend," said Smelly Socks,
"Do you know that you tickle?"

Smelly Socks and Hairy Legs
Spent all day in the shoe;
At bedtime, when they took it off
Said Hairy (in the loo)
"Phew!"

Louis the Sandwich

Louis the Sandwich is the kind
That no one wants to eat,
Everyone turns their nose up –
He tastes like smelly feet.

"What's wrong with him? Is he gone off?"
The people stand and stare;
"In God's name, what's he made of?
Some kind of Camembert?"

Louis the Sandwich sits alone
In the sandwich tray,
No one's going to take him
Today or any day.

He sits alone in the sandwich tray
Beside those made of cheddar:
"Why can't I be cheddar, too?" he sobs,
"And then I'd feel much better."

But Louis the Sandwich sits alone
In the sandwich tray –
No one's going to take him
Today or any day . . .

I'm the Horse's Bum in the Panto

I'm the horse's bum in the panto
(At least I've a part in the play);
I'm the horse's bum in the panto
(My friend at the head gets to neigh).

I'm the horse's bum in the panto
(At least they gave me a part);
Although I'm the bum and they tease me, by gum!
I'm in it! On stage! It's a start!

I'd Like To Be

I'd like to be a fat green snot
Snailing down your lip –
A silken, soupy, slimy snot
Dribble, dribble, drip!

You'd squelch me in through your front teeth,
Roll me round a bit
Then suck me back to shoot me out;
A swirling, swollen spit.

At the Seaside

When you paddle
In the sea
First you shiver
Then you pee
And the waves
That licked your toes
Suddenly
Fizz up your nose
And you stumble
Oh the shock
And you swallow water
Yock
But it's sweaty summer weather
And it's great fun altogether

Sea World

I'm a shark and I live in the shark tank,
Nothing to do all day long
But swim over and back;
My life's grim and black
And then someone like you comes along.

You look in with fish eyes through the shark tank –
Do you think I have no more to do
Than watch through the glass
You fish-eyed kids pass?
By God, but I'd like to eat **YOU**!

Percy the Hamster

Our Percy sleeps among shavings,
Shavings we buy cut from wood;
He makes a bed of the shavings,
He sleeps among shavings real good;

But one day he got hold of a *J-Cloth*,
He pulled it right into his cage,
And he chopped it and chewed it, and shook it and strewed it
All over the floor of his cage;

And there it soaks up all his wee-wees
I clean at the end of the week,
And he's brought some *J-Cloth* to his bed-box
And he burrows beneath for his sleep.

For he mixes *J-Cloth* with his shavings –
It's cosy, it's better than wood,
And he sleeps through the day in a comical way
Under *J-Cloth* and shavings and food!

Puppy and the Sausage

He thinks that it's fighting back
When it burns his nose;
He prances all about it
Barking, making shows.

He snaps at it, but it's too hot;
Tosses it up high,
Then stops to sniff and study it
Pawing nervously.

Now suddenly, the burning cooled,
Here comes the last attack;
He grabs it in his baby teeth
And gulps the sausage back.

Puppy Love

Puppy's got a girlfriend:
He groans and whines all day,
He barks and cries all through the night
As if he'd pine away.

Puppy's got a girlfriend:
But now they cannot meet –
His girlfriend's in confinement
Because she is in heat.

He cannot sit, he can't stand still;
The games we used to play
Are no good to Puppy now –
He just howls and pants all day.

Puppy's got a girlfriend:
He's completely out of sorts –
Delicious pain it seems to be,
Oh! how his girlfriend hurts.

Panting, panting, panting,
Last night he ate clean through
The softwood of his kennel door –
That's what love will do.

When we got up this morning,
He'd almost broken out;
So we brought him to the kitchen,
His hot tongue hanging out.

Panting, yelping, panting,
He's completely out of sorts;
Delicious pain! he loves it!
Oh! how his girlfriend hurts.

West Highland Terrier

Mam puts Fluffy in the bath,
He's dirty as old spuds;
He shivers first, then wags his tail,
And then he drinks the suds!

And when he's shampooed wet and white
He's hardly there at all,
But when he's dry his hair puffs out
Into a fluffy ball –
He's like a sheep, so woolly
Except that he is small.

Sandy
(for John)

1

Sandy is our dog,
A labrador.
We've had him since he was a pup;
We called him "Sandy"
'Cos he's sandy-coloured.

He's big
And strong
And I sleep on him sometimes
In the evening in the sun.

When I say "Sandy, come to Johnny,"
He runs to me;
When I say "Bedtime, Sandy,"
He goes to bed.

We made a run for Sandy –
Chain-link, four feet high;
We wanted him to be happy
In his run
But Sandy jumped it.
We were proud of him when he jumped:
We all laughed
To see Sandy jumping four-foot wire.

But we couldn't keep him
'Cos we were getting a calf.
Sandy needed freedom.
I cried and cried.

Daddy hugged me,
Mammy hugged me too;
Nessa wanted another dog
Instead of Sandy.

Daddy told me he knew the pain
Of missing Sandy –
His mammy died;
His daddy killed a goose
That was his friend
For Christmas dinner
And he had to eat it.

Mammy and Daddy read to me;
They promised me good things,
But I'll miss Sandy.

Dad said he'd write a poem
For Sandy.
A big poem,
Big as Sandy.

That cheered me up:
A poem that could jump a four-foot wire,
A poem that could jump even higher,
Over my sadness.

All I want now
Is that Sandy gets
Someone to love him,
To give him a good home,
To give Sandy a place that he can roam.

Sandy come to Johnny
Goodbye Sandy
Goodbye

Goodbye

2

The calf came.
We named her Dandelion.
She was six weeks old,
A Friesian, black-and-white.
We put her in Sandy's run.

We kept Sandy overnight
And in the morning, before we went to school,
Dad chained Sandy in the lawn –
It was a fourteen-foot chain
So Sandy could play
Fourteen feet each way.

When we came home,
Dad set Sandy free.
Sandy didn't bother Dandelion.
When 'twas time to feed her,
Dad brought Sandy up to see;

She drank her *Bloom*
(That's milk replacer)
And Sandy just looked on;
He wasn't jealous at all.
Mam said we could keep Sandy,
That he'd behave himself.

So, by day
Sandy has fourteen feet to play,
And in the evening, after three,
Sandy plays with Nessa and me.

Sandy come to Johnny
Good boy Sandy
Good boy

Good boy

A Sleepless Night

9 pm last Sunday –
Sandy watered, fed:
It's "Go to bed now, Sandy";
Sandy goes to bed.

2 am – he's barking.
Dad gets out of bed,
Takes him from his kennel
And puts him in the shed –

Lots more room for Sandy
But still he barks and barks.
Dad gets out of bed again
And shivers across the yard

In bare feet and pyjamas;
Opens up the shed,
Releases Sandy for a run
And then goes back to bed.

At 3 am he wakes again
To Sandy's *bark, bark, bark;*
Daddy groans, gets out of bed
And tiptoes through the dark

Calling "Sandy, Sandy, Sandy;"
Sandy runs to him
And Dad thinks of another plan –
He brings Sandy in.

He puts him in the bathroom
So he won't be in the dark,
He leaves the electric light switched on
So he won't have to bark
(He thinks that maybe Sandy's
Reacting to the dark).

Sandy goes to the toilet bowl,
Drinks some water there;
Dad closes the bathroom door on him,
Breathes a little prayer

That Sandy'll go to sleep now.
He goes back to bed
But Sandy starts to whimper –
First low, and then out loud,

And then he starts to barking.
Daddy shakes his head
(Mam's fast asleep beside him);
He gets out of bed –

It's 4 o'clock, he's got no sleep,
He brings Sandy to my room:
"Sandy, *SIT*! Now go to sleep,"
I hear my Daddy yawn.

But Sandy jumps up on my bed,
I'm wide awake as he –
"John, go to sleep with Mammy,"
Daddy says to me.

Dad lies in beside him
And Sandy settles down,
He licks Dad's face and ears and hands
Which takes away Dad's frown.

Sandy now is sleeping
But Dad can't get a wink;
He twists and turns, he says his prayers,
He gets up for a drink.

5 o'clock and Dad at last
Drifts into a sleep;
Dad curled like a baby,
Sandy in a heap

Beside him in my double bed –
My doggy and my dad.
When we wake up in the morning
Daddy isn't mad –

He thinks it's a bit funny,
I think it's funny, too
But Mam says, "What about my sheets?"
Says Dad, "What could I do?"

"What could I do?" he asks again
"He barked all through the night –
'Twas the only way to get some sleep."
And Mammy says, "All right".

My Goldfish

Goldie's swimming backwards –
No matter how I try,
I can't get him to swim properly.
I think he's going to die.

I flick him with my finger
But to no avail,
He seems to only use his fins
And not his tail.

Goldie's swimming backwards,
I think I'm going to cry –
He's never swum like this before.
Oh, Goldie, please don't die.

The Dead Wasp

There I was
Buzzing about my business
When *Wham!*
This big guy swats me to the ground
And stands on me.
I crack and die.
Why?

Why do big guys kill us?
We mean no harm.

Is it because they're afraid
We'll sting them?
They fear and kill,
We die.

Why do people kill the things they fear?
Why?

There's a Snake Inside in Our Toilet

There's a snake inside in our toilet –
I saw him there staring at me;
There's a snake inside in our toilet –
I have to go out for a wee.

There's a snake inside in our toilet,
The TV said he's someone's pet
That got into the pipes while escaping
And the snake-man's not captured him yet.

There's a snake inside in our toilet,
I can't, I just can't use the loo –
If there was a snake down your toilet,
You'd be afraid to go too.

There's a snake inside in our toilet –
I saw him there looping the loop;
I can't, I just can't use the toilet –
We have to use potties for poops.

There's a snake inside in our toilet –
No one here uses the jacks;
Oh, snake-man, come quick and please catch him
And take this embarrassment back!

Of Cats and Daddies

Cats have ways around humans –
If you meet a cat what's astray,
You feed him because he looks lonely
And you're glad when he'll trust you and stay.

Cats have ways around humans
(But there's something that I must tell you –
I have ways around Daddy:
He does what I ask him to do).

Cats have ways around humans.
I can make Daddy give me –
Love won't refuse a small kitten
And Daddy's just mad about me!

Patrick Had a Little Dog

Patrick had a little dog,
Snowy was his name;
He followed him to school one day
And joined in every game.

He played at lunch-time with the kids
And only left them when
The teachers chased him from the yard.
But he came back again!

His First Day at School

"Hello! And who might you be?
You're playing a lovely game –
Can I join in and play with you?
Tell me, what's your name?"

"John," he vaguely tells me.
"John what?" He's puzzled now,
He doesn't know his other name.
(I'll find out somehow.)

"Have you any brothers or sisters?"
(An only child it seems)
"Have you any cousins in this school?"
He has, he gives their names:
There's Joan and Tom, another John
Who sometimes play his games.

"Who's your dad? What's Daddy's name?"
(Dad's first name will do,
It's all I need to place him now,
The final clue.)

"What's Daddy's name?" I ask again;
He thinks, and then he beams.
"Daddy! That's my daddy's name,"
And scuppers all my schemes.

Cinderella

"Today we're going to do a play."
"Yippee! Miss Gunn, yippee!"
The children shout and jump about.
(What part will she give me?)

"You'll be Cinderella,
You'll be the King's son –
The one they call Prince Charming,
And you can be (now, let me see) –
A bun!

The bun that Cinderella makes
That walks and talks and sings."
*(A bun like that is not so bad
I'll do lots of things)*

So in the play, he buns away . . .
What's this? – he stops up dead!
And cries, "Miss Gunn, I'm not a bun –
There's no currant on my head!"

My Teddy

School is big and strange and scary,
I take Teddy by the hands
And, though I'm teased and called a fairy,
Teddy understands.

And when the girls and boys are ready
And I'm behind at all commands,
I look across and smile at Teddy
'Cos Teddy understands.

And I cuddle him, so lonely,
'Cos he loves me and demands
Nothing of me but me only
'Cos Teddy understands.

The Man in the Tennis Court

"There's a man in the tennis court with his head in a drain
And we can't get him out," she said;
The teacher stops in her tracks, and fears
The caretaker must be dead.

"How well 'twould happen to me," she thinks,
"First thing in the morning alone;
I could have stayed drinking a cup of tea
Another five minutes at home."

"There's a man in the tennis court with his head in a drain."
She sends her class around;
The gate is locked, they can't get in,
And this is what they've found –

They stampede back to their teacher then
And in one voice they shout
"There's a plastic Power Ranger with his head in the drain
And the infants can't get him out!"

The Pencil Pointer

Ger the Pencil Pointer
Points and points all day
(All day pointing pencils,
No time at all for play)

With a round one and a square one
And a fat one with a box
Where all the pencil pointings
Pile up as they drop.

He points in class, at playtime,
And when the kids come in
Ger the Pencil Pointer
Is over at the bin

Pointing, pointing pencils
Or emptying the box –
He never seems to write with them
(He chews the pencil tops)

Pointing, pointing, pointing,
He'll point until he drops,
He wishes someone would invent
A bigger pointing box.

A Painful Experience

Let's beat him up!
I said it.
I only meant to frighten him;
He's so annoying,
Everybody hates him,
But Big Bob thought I meant it
And punched him in the chest.
That's all that happened –
One punch in the chest,
But Billy cried.
He didn't cry 'cos Big Bob hurt him
But he was hurt.

I hurt him.
If I hadn't opened my big mouth
This wouldn't have happened;
Big Bob wouldn't have hit him
And I wouldn't be in trouble.

I'm in trouble with the teacher,
But, worse
I'm in trouble with myself –
I feel bad about it.
Why didn't I keep my big mouth shut?
I didn't hit him
But I hurt him –
More than any punch, I hurt him.

I don't really like him,
He annoys me
But I'm sorry that I hurt him.
It isn't right.
Now I feel bad about it.

I'm sorry, Billy,
Sorry.

(If my words hurt him
Maybe they'll take the hurt away)

I'm sorry, Billy,
Sorry.
Let's play.

Playtime

We were playing this game in the yard, sir,
Tip the Can, it was;
We were all having great fun, sir,
When Roger comes along
And says, "This game is boring,
Let's play *Red Rover.*"
You know *Red Rover,* sir –
It's only for babies.

Well, *Tip the Can* was my game
And everyone was happy playing it
But when Roger said, "Let's play *Red Rover,*"
Everyone left and played it.
Everyone follows Roger.
It's not fair.
We were all playing my game, sir,
Happily out there.

So I came into the classroom, sir,
To sit here by myself.
Why does everyone follow Roger?
Roger is my friend
But I hate him when he breaks up games;
I feel like punching him,
Calling him names.

Please, sir,
Can I stay in the classroom
Till playtime's over?

The Great Man is Coming

The Great Man is coming, the Great Man is coming,
The Great Man is coming today –
He's coming from Town, and on his way down
He'll visit our school, people say.

The Great Man is coming, the Great Man is coming,
The Great Man is coming today
And we have it planned that we'll form in a band
And greet him and shout *Hip Hooray!*

The Great Man is here, the Great Man is here,
He's in Mossie's Lounge Bar up the street
To pay his respects and be photographed with
Old soldiers who won us this peace.

The Great Man is coming, the Great Man is coming –
The Great Man has stopped at the gate
And we all run out, we cheer and we shout
But his handlers say he's running late.

The Great Man must go, the Great Man must go,
He's expected for photos, he's late!
So he gets in the Merc (it's one of his perks)
And he leaves us for dead at the gate.

And we wave and we cheer as he pulls out of here
While his escort speeds on ahead,
But I'll never forget being betrayed at the gate
The day that he left us for dead.

Praise

Everything I do they say is brilliant
Although I know it's no good at all myself;
They hang my pictures up like they're Picassos,
Display all my models on the shelf.

They think I don't realise they're fooling me –
This kind of praise is not the praise I need:
This kind of praise insults me, it's so phony;
The kind of praise I want is praise indeed.

You praise me, I can't trust you – do you mean it?
Meaning well, you praise my worst attempt;
Encourage me, but *please* don't patronize me;
The praise I need is praise I know that's meant.

Homework

The teacher's suspicious – I got my sums right;
He doesn't believe that I did them last night.
He says that I copied, he tries and he tries
To force me to say that I'm telling him lies.
He blushes with temper and lets out a roar,
Marches me roughly out on the floor
And tells me, by God! that he'll get to the truth,
That he doesn't know what's become of the youth.
He tells me I copied, and when I deny
He presses and presses till I start to cry,
Then speaks to me gently; I do as I'm bid –
He asks if I copied, and I say I did.

My Song

I was the worst boy in my class,
Stupid, ugly, fat;
No one expected anything of me.
Useless at my lessons,
Didn't do PE,
I copied at tests
And they let me.
(They couldn't be bothered
Even about that.)

So we did our tests.
I was "weak" at reading,
"Weak" at maths,
A token "very good" at art.
(The teacher trying to be nice to me.)

When 'twas time for singing
I blushed;
We had to sing one verse of any song.
I'd never sung in class before
(I never sing in class,
Just keep quiet while the others sing)
No one expected me to,
But I sang –
Not a song from school
(I don't know any songs from school)
But a song from long ago
That Granda sings.

The boys and girls paid no attention
But the teacher came alive –
"Where did you get that song?" he asked me,
"I've been looking for it a long time", he said,
"Would you sing it again?"

I sang it again for him
And he whistled as I sang;
He asked me to write out the words for him.
Jeezus! I smiled and smiled.
Maybe I'm not useless –
The teacher came alive,
He whistled my song all evening.
Tears came in his eyes;
He pulled a face to hide it
But I saw him nearly cry.

I surprised the teacher –
That surprised the girls and boys.

I'm big and fat –
Not ugly,
I'm no good at school
But once I taught the teacher
I know I'm not a fool.

Mistakes

"You *paddle* a bike,"
(I mean *pedal*)
"A fish will swim with its *wings*,"
(I mean *fins*)
When Daddy first said not to *meddle*
I thought I'd won it –
Now I just laugh at such things:

Mistakes I made as a youngster,
Mistakes I don't make now at all
'Cos now that I'm eight
(It's *great* to be eight!)
I'm not such a ninny at all.

A Christmas Fable

"I'm arresting you," the policeman said –
"Breaking and entering when all's abed;
Whoever you are, you must keep the laws.
What's your name?"
"I'm Santa Claus."
"You're Santa Claus!" the policeman said –
"Santa Claus, like God, is dead,
A bait for kids in the Superstore;
We don't believe in you any more."

"I'm arresting you," the policeman said,
"The children here must be protected
From men with beards and gaudy suits –
We must protect them from abuse.
They're taken in by men like you –
Santa, boy, we're on to you.
Do you think you can destroy
My cushy beat with a paltry toy?
I've seen your kind 'round here before –
They're serving time behind locked doors."

"Without me," says Santa Claus,
"There's no point in having laws,
For, if you don't believe in good,
Why keep the law in servitude?
And for all the girls and boys
Christmas would be merely toys
Purchased in the Superstore
Where money talks. Yet you ignore
Everything that Santa is –
What is this new paralysis?

Your Santa Claus is dead, *kaput!*
Your doors are locked, your heart is shut
For, once you've lost your Santa Claus,
There's no point in having laws."

Santa Claus holds out his hands –
The policeman doesn't understand;
Yet, moved by some forgotten dream,
He grunts: "If you're what you seem,
There's no reason for alarm;
The likes of you will do no harm."
He uncocks his torch, turns off the light –
"Goodnight, Mister Santa Claus."
"Goodnight."

Singing Lesson

Will we sing?
No, I'm too shy
Well I know it –
So am I;

So, when I sing
I close my eyes
Till there's nothing
But my voice,

Nothing but
My voice and I –
Inside I'm singing,
Outside I'm shy;

So close your eyes
And look within,
Then open up
And sing, sing, sing . . .

Blossoming

Little buds upon a tree
Blossom forth eventually
Like me

First they open then they bloom
Pushing out to make more room
Like me

And they flower as they please
And their beauty feeds the bees
Like me

Yes the blossoms flower and fruit
Growing into their own truth
Like me

Thank you God for me